Flat bottom

Flat bottom

Connect lines

Connect lines

Keep open

Keep open

Make definite cross

Make definite cross

Make a definite x

Make a definite x

Two straight lines

Two straight lines

Two closed loops

Two closed loops

THE SECRET HEART
of NUMBERS

Photographs
and Text
by
Dirk Wales

Sourcebooks
Inc.
Naperville, Illinois

Published by: **Sourcebooks, Inc.**
P.O. Box 372, Naperville, Illinois 60566
(708) 961-3900
FAX: 708-961-2168

Editorial: Todd Stocke
Interior Production: Wayne Johnson

Publisher's Note:
This is a work of fiction. Names, characters, places, and incidents either are the product of the author's imagination or, if real, are used fictitiously, and any resemblance to actual persons, living or dead, events, or locales is entirely coincidental.

"God's Billy Pulpit," by Nancy Gibbs and Richard Ostling, November 15, 1993, © 1993 Time Inc. Reprinted by permission.

Library of Congress Cataloging-in-Publication Data

Wales, Dirk
      The secret heart of numbers/
Dirk Wales.
        p.   cm.
      ISBN 1-57071-053-8 (hc) : $16.95
      1. Numbers--Fiction. 2. Numbers--Pictorial works. I. Title.
PS3573.A42347S4   1996
813'.54--dc20

                                                      95-30441
                                                       CIP

Printed and bound in the United States of America.
10 9 8 7 6 5 4 3 2 1

This book is dedicated to

my number two.

	1	2	3	4	5	6	7	8	9
10	11	12	13	14	15	16	17	18
19	20	21	22	23	24	25	26	27
28	29	30	31	32	33	34	35	36
37	38	39	40	41	42	43	44	45
46	47	48	49	50	51	52	53	54
55	56	57	58	59	60	61	62	63
64	65	66	67	68	69	70	71	72
73	74	75	76	77	78	79	80	81
82	83	84	85	86	87	88	89	90
91	92	93	94	95	96	97	98	99

I am caught up in numbers.

17, my birthdate.

18, the number of my high school football jersey.

My army serial number...04027681 (Sir).

My need to play 16 or 19 on the roulette wheel.

I can't live without numbers.

They say Van Gogh

was ambivalent about numbers.

Are we ruled by numbers?

Engineers have slide rules,
Carpenters unfold yardsticks.
Telescopes sweep the skies, counting the stars.
All measurements of a sort.

But, Tony will always be the 13th child.
Jessica will always be the second.

23 will always be Joel's lucky number,
the one he played basketball in…
and Amy will always be his first love,
though they are not together now.

Numbers are pathways to the heart.
The tides come in on schedule.

11 is the number of my lost love.

She couldn't stand the idea of one (person)
and one (person) in love making One. Too scary!
But, she knew that romantically Two was not the right number.
So, I told her that for us it would be 11.

One beside one made 11.

She liked that, but she ran away anyway.

                    No number was strong enough to hold her.

Think of all the numbers that own you.

Your Amex card: 3781 62 8223 21005;

your UAL Premier card: 00124 757 213;

your Master Charge card: 5242 0021 0610 8132;

your seats at the Concert Hall, C-9 and C-10;

your Captain Video membership number: 26767;

your fax number: (505) 820-6334 (FAX never sleeps);

your #One Club number: GM931w;

your Statue of Liberty/Ellis Island Foundation, Inc., number...

She's about to embark on marriage No. 3.

Marriage number one doesn't count because

"Blah-blah-blah-blah-blah-blah-"

Marriage number two doesn't count because

"Blah-blah-blah-blah-blah-blah-"

So, she said, marriage No. 3 is really

Marriage number One.

Who's counting?

Everyone!

Would you take a chance on Number Four?

NORTH

(Which number is lucky?)

(Which number is not real?)

WEST

1	2	3	4	5	6	7	8	9	10	11
12	13	14	15	16	17	18	19
20	21	22	23	24	25	26	27
28	29	30	31	32	33	34	35
36	37	38	39	40	41	42	43
44	45	46	47	48	49	50	51
52	53	54	56	57	58	59	60
61	62	63	64	65	66	67	68
69	70	71	72	73	74	75	76
77	78	79	80	81	82	83	84
85	86	87	88	89	90	91	92
93	94	95	96	97	98	99	100

(Which number mystifies you?)

EAST

SOUTH

(Which number is magic?)

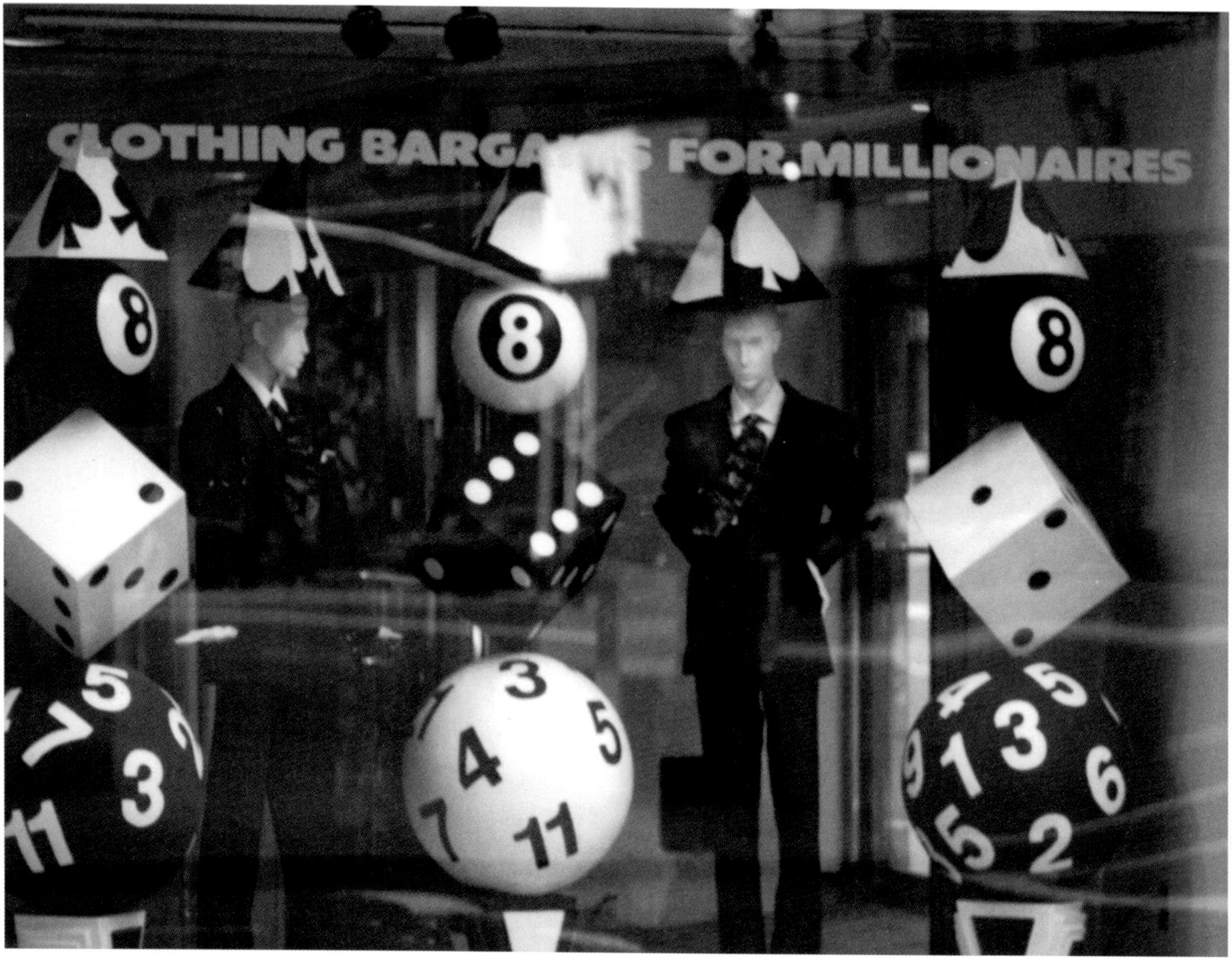
CLOTHING BARGA
S FOR MILLIONAIRES

When I get excited about numbers,
I just add zeros.

1 2 3 4 5 6 7 8 9 10 11 12 13 14 15 16 17 18 19 20

The winning number is right

21 22 23 24 25 26 27 28 29 30 31 32 33 34 35 36 37

beside the losing number.

The woman found the ball at the beach.

It was an odd ball for it had a circular queue
of numbers all the way around the sphere.

All her life she had been afraid of numbers.
In school, at work, even in her marriage she avoided them:
she made her husband pay the bills, and when they were old enough,
she made her kids go to the supermarket for her.

She tried to throw the ball away.
She would throw it far out in the surf
so the undertow would carry it out to sea,
away from her.

But, the ball kept coming back to her, and every time it did,
she needed to pick it up and hold it to return it to the sea.

Each time she held it, she became more comfortable with the ball.
Though the sea was chilly, the ball was warm.
No matter how she held it, the ball caught the sunlight and gleamed.

She rubbed it with her fingers and found the numbers were raised
so that she could feel the shape of each number:
1 and 2 and 3, and all the way to 9 and zero.

Finally she noticed that the ball had stars on it.

"Two stars," she thought, and took it home
wondering if she could explain how the ball came to be hers.

numbers count us up

10 10  1 1
9 9 2 2
8 8 3 3
7 7 4 4
6 6 5 5

5 5   6 6

4 4   7 7

3 3   8 8

2 2   9 9

1 1   10 10

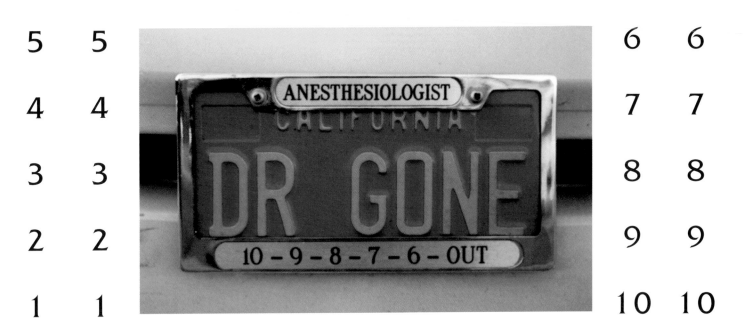

numbers count us out

The cynic says that numbers have no souls.
As if numbers were heavy, grounded...
as if numbers had never flowed from the pen of the skywriter.

The idealist says that numbers have souls.
That it's people who are grounded and heavy!
After all, it's latitude and longitude that grip the earth.
How could 32°41" be grounded?
It floats over Easter Island keeping a line on the statues.

And, who knows, there may be a Numbers Angel.

There is a timekeeper inside all clocks.

This is not Father Time or the Hunchback of Notre Dame.

It's a vision of yourself…

the one who sees that you are always five minutes early,

or always 20 minutes late,

or dependably the punctual one.

Who's counting?

The final equanimity of numbers
is they can be themselves even
when they are upside down:

88   96

L U C K Y N U M B E R

1 2 3 4 5 6 7 8 9 10 11

12 13 14 15 16 17 18 19 20 21 22

23 24 25 26 27 28 29 30 31 32 33

34 35   36 37

38 39   y o u r   40 41

42 43   n u m b e r   44 45

46 47   h e r e   48 49

50 51   52 53

54 55 56 57 58 59 60 61 62 63 64

65 66 67 68 69 70 71 72 73 74 75

76 77 78 79 80 81 82 83 84 85 86

87 88 89 90 91 92 93 94 95 96 97

98   99

Think of the numbers that own you!

Your health insurance card: L-34216 (61272 0054),

to verify coverage, call 1 800 247 4699;

your New Mexico Motor Club number: 3187721-12;

your Metropolitan Museum of Art membership number: 67005581;

your Museum of Modern Art membership number: d70008531;

your Coconuts Video number: CH11126;

the number for your cat at the vet's: 17;

your secretary's home telephone number: 787 0571;

your ex-wife's home...

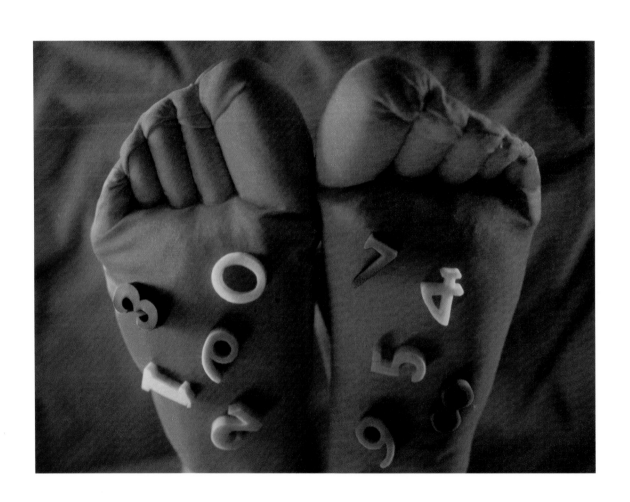

I knew a man who had numbers tattooed on his feet—
the bottoms.
He had come from far away.
He was looking for a woman who had numbers
on the bottoms of her feet—just like his.
I told him we have no women with numbers
on the bottoms of their feet.

He said, "That's what you think!"

"Imaginary numbers! Don't be ridiculous!!"

In 1492, the same year that Columbus sailed for America, there was a debate in Seville between two mathematicians. What the Judge of the Debate did not know is that they were also secret lovers. To the Judge, they seemed to hate each other, so acid were their arguments.

Her position was that imaginary numbers existed. His was that not only did they not exist, but that she was a fool to advocate this premise. The battle ranged over fields of mathematics...as if these two numbers jugglers had set all the combinations of 1, 2, 3, 4, 5, 6, 7, 8, 9, 0 in motion on a battleplane as vast as Spain itself.

In the end, she sat calmly in her padded chair and said, "Then, pose me this, Sirra, I have a lonely number in mind. Can you tell me what is the square root of -2?"

After four hours of wasted parchment, he gave in... encouraged by the Judge that he had lost, that imaginary numbers existed, and that she was a greater wizard in mathematics than he.

As she left the Court of Debate, passing his table, the point of her finger drew a faint and gentle line along the top of his hand.

An old woman did my name in numbers once.
She said I had a lucky number name,
but not to gamble or marry a woman whose
numbers add up to 9.

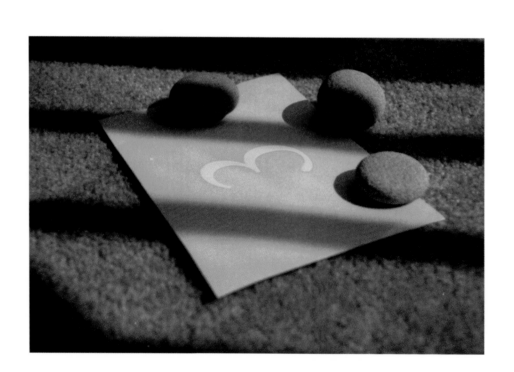

Numbers breathe with us and we with them.
They are as basic to us as light and water and stone.

The stars are too far away.

1 2 3 4 5 6 7 8 9 10 11

12 13 14 15 16 <u>17</u> 18 19

20 21 22 23 24 25 26 27

28 29 30 31 32 33 34 35

36 37 38 39 40 41 42 43

44 45 46 47 48 49 50 51

52 53 54 55 56 57 58 59

60 61 62 63 64 65 66 67

68 69 70 71 72 73 74 75

76 77 78 79 80 81 82 83

84 85 86 87 88 89 90 91

92 93 (94) 95 96 97 98 99

Grandmother lived to be 94.

That was the number she quilted into her
blanket when she was 17.

If your days are numbered,

count slowly…

1. I

 8. until

 2. never

 9. Mary

 3. thought

 10. Dawson

 4. of

 11. told

 5. numbers

 12. me

 6. as

 13. she

 7. sexual

 14. made

15. a

 22. she

 16. long

 23. ever

 17. list

 24. slept

 18. of

 25. with

 19. all

26.

 20. the

 21. men

1   2   3   4   5

How many secrets are burning a hole inside you?

6   7   8   9

I was a cadet when I turned Sweet 16.
My birthday was on the 17th, and I was playing football with 18
on my back. After I had blown out the birthday candles, no one
actually said, "Sweet 16 and never been kissed."
But, I had been kissed.

Three times…

The first kiss came from Mary Cottle,
the only person in the world shyer than I.

The third from Connie McWhirter: I have never
been so frightened by the opposite sex...

The kiss in the middle?

A mystery woman, aged 15, whose name
I never discovered...in a closet playing sardines
in Oceanside, California.

On my birthday, I thought...3 kisses in 16 years.
That means that in my whole life
there may be only 9 more!

I fell in love once with a woman who loved numbers—money.

She thought about it all the time.

For a joke, one Halloween,
I dressed myself (only) in dollar bills.

That night, she made love to me as she never had before.

So, I knew.

WONDERS

BRIDES

VEILS

7	7	7	7	7	7	7
7	7	7	7	7	7	7
7	7	7	7	7	7	7
7	7	7	7	7	7	7
7	7	7	7	7	7	7
7	7	7	7	7	7	7
7	7	7	7	7	7	7

SEAS * SINS

"Numbers, poets complain, are soulless things, the anonymous rungs of infinity. But, it is hard to talk about Billy Graham, the great reaper of souls, without talking about numbers. This is the man who has preached in person to more people than any human being who has ever lived. What began in country churches and trailer parks and circus tents moved through cathedrals and stadiums and the world's vast public squares, where he has called upon more than 100,000,000 people to 'accept Jesus Christ as your Personal Savior.'"

Nancy Gibbs
Richard N. Ostling
<u>Time</u> Magazine, 1993

The question has come up about
what Jesus may have thought about numbers...

One God
Two of Everything
Trinity
Four Saints
Seven Days
Ten Commandments
Thirteen for Dinner
One Judas

I admire numbers.
They are so secure, so individual.

1 is always 1.
2 would never pretend to be 7.
9 would not wish to join the alphabet
and become Q.

Numbers have integrity.

Kathy learned to paint-by-the-numbers before
she was in Kindergarten.
Her mother said she had an instinctive flair for numbers.
Kathy decided she would live-and-love-by-the-numbers!

She met a man at a costume party.
He was dressed as number 36.
She loved that and decided to marry him two weeks later.

The next year they were invited to the same
party and her husband, without telling her,
changed his costume to number 81.
Kathy left him early the next morning.
She said he was playing fast and loose with their numbers.

...it's one of those statistic books. You know,
the sort of tome that puts everything into perspective
in terms that can be understood down to the decimal point:

    a. The average man spends 74.1 hours
        buttoning his shirts in his lifetime.

    b. The number of nail clippings in an average
        life, men or women, weighs 1,483.27 pounds.

    c. There are 891.7 seconds of orgasm in every
        male life, 1,048.9 in every female life
        (who says the feminist revolution didn't work!).

    d. Finally, if we counted the number of Twinkies
        that were consumed since the inception of Twinkies
        in 1937...(in Canarsy, New York)...the latest one
        eaten, at the 5th Grade cook-out of Damon School
        in Exeter Park, Mass., the final Twinkies count
        would be 3,761,542,002.

Who's counting?

94. false Truth.

When party keys mix it up with Numbers

there's no telling

—after the party—

which key will open which door.

Have you noticed you never see numbers in the sky?

In the blue
you see only the ink blots of elephants,
mountains of cumulus,
and the breasts of women moving East.

Never a 9, not a dollar sign, no 2 4 6 8,
numbers are above all that.

Kathy is counting the number of times her husband has to work late.

Alfredo is counting his blessings.

There is a man in South Africa whose days are numbered.

The spirit of numbers is the way they Dance...
taunting you with the roulette of Life:

Red   Black
                    0 0
Odd   Even

Years of routine, seconds of pleasure.

A boy was given, at birth, an extra hour of life.
          60 minutes. 3,600 seconds.

When he was young, he used them on frivolous things:
magic, pleasure, tricks on his parents, and when he
was 19, he created the ultimate orgasm for himself
and his girlfriend: 4 minutes and 23 seconds.
The girl told her friends and he became an
instant folk hero.

But, he thought, I have wasted much. He measured
his maturity from the moment when he counted
meaningful numbers instead of meaningless numbers.

He began to save minutes and seconds. To count each
dearly. And, he set aside 8 seconds. He would
decide at what moment in his life (and who would be
with him when) he would stop everything in the universe
to find a crack in time that would explain
the meaning of life.

Eight seconds was all it would take, he calculated.

Sometimes I'm afraid of numbers.

And, sometimes it feels like Numbers are
playing tricks
on us.

1   2   3   4   5   6   7   8   9   0

If there are fun numbers…

birthday candles

alimony

an I. R. A.

the lottery

a bull market

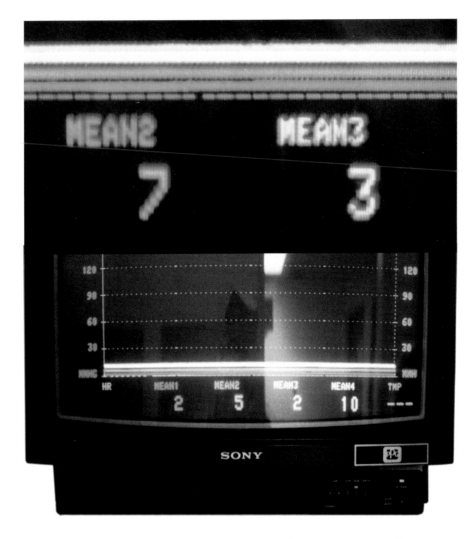

...there have to be mean numbers
birthday candles
alimony
the I. R. S.
the lottery
a bear market

Two means together. Two means twice.
Sometimes two means a second chance.

In a family, two is the second child.
In mine, it was <u>my</u> sister.
She was much funnier than I, smarter too.
Taller by 2/10ths of an inch, and slimmer...
lovely to look at in pink and yellow.

We were together once by a river in Leadville, Colorado.
She said, "let's take a dip," and we stripped there and then.
She was what the Texans call a bone hungry lovely woman.
She was, indeed. In the river we splashed and had a time.

I miss that time, and all the times with her.
She was my number two.

She was never born.

The young man was an MBA candidate at Harvard. He had promise. A 'numbers wiz,' they called him. 'Natural born numbers cruncher,' they predicted.

What a future!

But, the young man and his girlfriend, a philosophy major at Wellesley, knew that he had bottom line anxieties. He might be the best analytical numbers juggler in the school, but he had trouble committing to that ever-necessary bottom line.

Just before finals, she invited him to dinner
at the beach. After dinner, she took him to
a deserted cove and took off all her clothes.

As she faced him, she said, "Listen, I love
you and I want to help you get through this..."
and she turned around.

Across her buttocks she had a long black line
tattooed. "This is the only bottom line you'll
ever have to be committed to."

She counted his kisses. He counted her kisses.
They counted other things they did together...
One day, they stopped keeping score.
Then came uncounted blessings.

She was the sort of person whose character depended
on which side of the bed she arose from:
east or west, right or left, good or bad.

She was having an affair with a man.
On Friday night, she invited him to stay for breakfast.
On Saturday, she got up on the east-right-good side.
On Sunday, she got up on the west-left-bad side.
He was quick enough to notice the difference.

On Monday, he managed to get her up on the east-right-good side.
"Just checking," he thought.
On Tuesday, he suggested they redecorate the bedroom.
The west-left-bad side of the bed ended up against the wall.

Her life changed.

They married and actually lived happily ever-after.

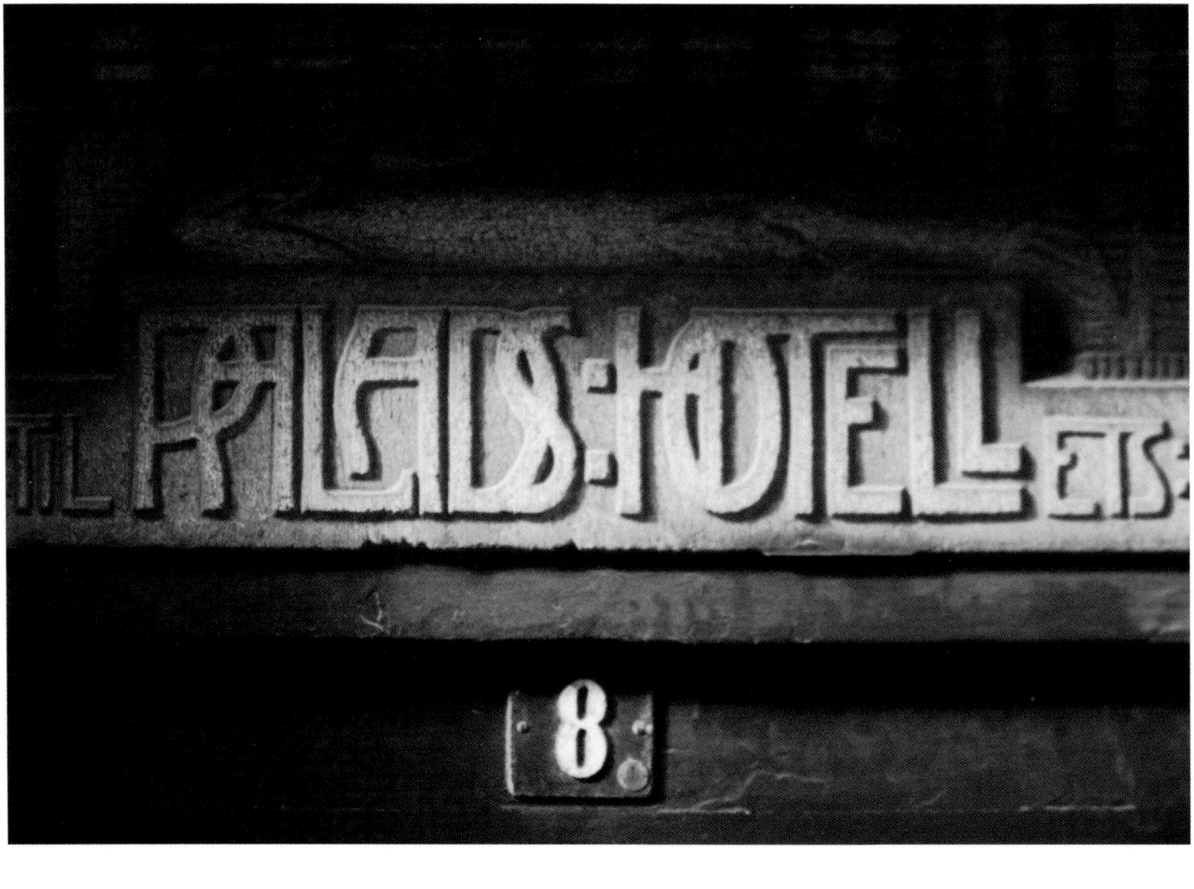
8

The author and publisher wish to thank the following people, whose valuable impressions and opinions helped create this book:

Pat Peterson, Barbara's Bookstore, Chicago; Jeff Rice, Great Expectations Bookstore, Evanston, IL; Helen Repp, 57th Street Bookstore, Chicago; Jack Cella, University of Chicago Seminary Co-op Bookstore; Dennis Gosselin, Chicago Tribune Magazine; Chris Newman, Chicago Magazine; Gretchen Helfrich, WBEZ, National Public Radio; Robert Clark Davis, School of the Art Institute of Chicago; Robert VonHallberg and Martha Ward, University of Chicago; Scott Kraft, Northwestern University Library; Liz Seaton, Northwestern University Block Gallery; Kevin Cassidy, Matt McClintock, and Emily Citrano, Columbia College, Chicago; Edward Wolpert, Rush Presbyterian Hospital at the University of Illinois at Chicago; Eric Miller, Juilliard School; and to Laura Sciortino for all her work.

Numbered eggs
Santa Fe, New Mexico

Bike riders
R.A.G.B.R.Y. across Iowa
(Thanks to Stacey Wales)

Complaint department
Fresno, California

13 (Van Gogh)
Van Gogh Museum,
Amsterdam, Holland

Dart
Las Vegas, Nevada

Woman carrying 2
Michigan Avenue, Chicago

Ruler
Elco, Nevada

Pencils and tabs
Chicago, Illinois

Mystic Ball
Malibu, California

Ferris wheel
Balboa Island, California

**Clothing bargains for
millionaires**
Madison Avenue,
New York, New York

Ball
Malibu, California

License plate house
Telluride, Colorado

100% T-Shirt
Bloomingdale's, Chicago

Coroner
Charleston, South Carolina

Dr. Gone
San Diego, California

A talking cat with 5
Chicago, Illinois

3 stones
Butte, Montana

SZ in the sky
San Francisco, California

Eleven cave
Madrid, New Mexico

08 10 12 Graveyard
Questa, New Mexico

Big clock
D'Orsay Museum, Paris,
France

Feet with numbers
No record

Self-portrait with 33
Lake Huron, North America

96
Osaka, Japan

-2 mural
Amsterdam, Holland

Clock
A collaboration between
Charlotte Ross and Dirk
Wales

00 infinity
SoHo, New York City

20 de Octubre
The San Blas Islands,
Caribbean Sea

Mary Dawson
Tesuque, New Mexico
(Thanks to The Shidoni Foundry)

4 with candles
Taos, New Mexico

Man with numbered face
Der Haag, Holland

Candles
New Orleans, Louisiana

3
Toronto, Ontario

Jesus' birthday cake
Oak Park, Illinois

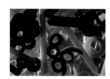

Party keys
New Orleans, Louisiana

Tom's firework shop
Between Charleston and
Savannah

Woman with 25 molé
San Blas Islands are 80
miles of the East Coast of
Panama

Clouds with no numbers
Cerrillos, New Mexico

Watching 0
New York City

**Photograph of a sketch of
a flaming 81**
Venice, California

0 road sign
Near Embudo Station, New
Mexico

7 miles from Lucea
Jamaica B.W.I.

94. false truth
San Francisco, California

5 o'clock
Spirit, Utah

8 on man
Portobello Road, London, England

Mysterious door (100)
Santa Fe, New Mexico

Prison
Cell of the Birdman of Alcatraz

1c 3a 2a 4c
Los Angeles, California

Pastel chalks
Thanks to Tom Petroff, Chicago, Illinois

Medical monitors
Pittsburgh, Pennsylvania

The 2 in my heart
Milford, Connecticut

3 with bobby pins
Marblehead, Massachusetts

3 is the bottom line
Marblehead, Massachusetts

Stamp
Oxford, England

9
Near Trafalgar Square, England

Numbers soup
Portobello Road, England

9
57th Street, New York City

8
Copenhagen, Denmark

7
Stockholm, Sweden

6
Geneva, Switzerland

0
Berlin, Germany

5
Kew Gardens, England

4
Detroit, Michigan

3, 2
Santa Fe, New Mexico

A-1
Farmington, New Mexico

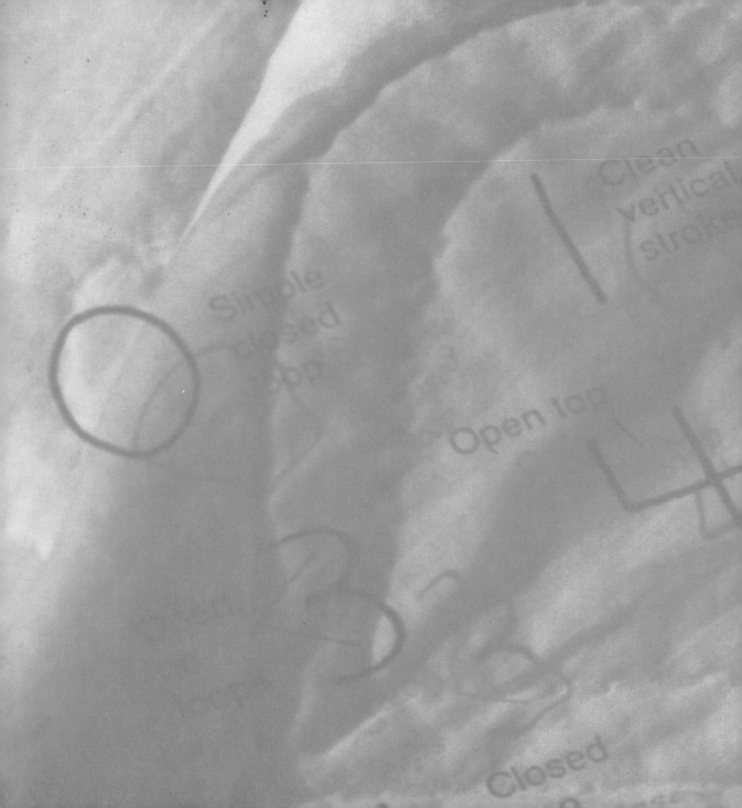